Park Storie

Park Stories: Along Birdcage Walk
© Clare Wigfall 2009

ISBN: 978-0-9558761-7-2

Series Editor: Rowan Routh

Published by The Royal Parks
www.royalparks.org.uk

Production by Strange Attractor Press
BM SAP, London, WC1N 3XX, UK
www.strangeattractor.co.uk

Cover design: Ali Hutchinson

Park Stories devised by Rowan Routh

The Royal Parks gratefully acknowledges the financial support of Arts Council England.

Printed by Kennet Print, Devizes, UK on 100% post-consumer recycled Cyclus offset paper using vegetable-based inks.

Along Birdcage Walk

Clare Wigfall

THE
ROYAL
PARKS

Along Birdcage Walk

Perhaps I should have read the signs; for truth, now that I look upon our tale I see that they were plain enough.

Did you know? Did you know before even you first met me? Or was it only later that the realisation came?

Now that I am alone, I wonder. As indeed I wonder, had I been privy to how events would unfold, would I have alter'd my course? Would I have risk'd not knowing what it was to love you? Not knowing what it was to be lov'd?

I first set eyes upon you along Birdcage Walk, whilst taking the air that summer afternoon in St James's Park. It was the year of our lord 1664. That avenue of trees has long delighted me. The treetops, bowing towards one another, form a corridor pleasantly cool in the summer heat, and for its full length, the branches are strung with gilded cages whose jewel-bright occupants set the air alive with exotic trills and squawks. Across the pathway peacocks strut, their tail feathers glittering the gravel in their wake, whilst even more curious creatures, gifted to our king by foreign ambassadors, preen their feathers and perch deep within the foliage – cassowaries, and green parrots, and strange pluméd fowl I cannot name. The smallest ones flutter gaily about their cages, their wings batting against the bars.

'Tis a place where, for an instant at least, one can forget the trials and tribulations of this life of ours.

That moment I first laid eyes upon you, you had your back to us with hands clasp'd behind you, leaning forwards as you whistl'd at a chaffinch on its perch. You were dress'd well, I could see that: your coat cut of a good cloth, your breeches fashion'd in a canary yellow silk.

As we passed, 'Good day,' said one in my party, and you turn'd. 'Good day to you.'

Your visage intrig'd me. Your face, caught in the freckl'd sunlight, was fine-boned, the skin pale with a near translucency much like a child's. Your glance was abstracted, distant. For but a fraction of a second did we hold your attention before, with a courteous nod, you turn'd back to the bird.

'Pray, who might that gentleman be?' I ask'd of my companions. I confess I was chagrin'd, and yet intrig'd, to have been unworthy of no more than this fleeting disinterest. As a young woman of not unbecoming appearance, with mine honour intact and a fortune worth two thousand a year, I was accustom'd to turning heads, and indeed accustom'd to ignoring them. Yet as we continued along the avenue, 'twas *I* who glanced back across my shoulder to see you standing yet alongside the cagéd bird, your face intent with observation, our party forgotten already.

I sought you out after that. I could not rid you from my mind. Each day I made excuse to return to Birdcage Walk until, one afternoon – happy chance – I found you once more. Again alone. Absorb'd still by the birds, as before.

'How pretty they are,' I commented, drawing close unto the cage which held your fascination. It housed four small songbirds, their coats a shiny indigo, the throat of one rais'd in song. In my chest my heart quiver'd, more frantic than the birds' wings against the metal bars. So loud it beat I fear'd you might observe it past his gay tune.

''Tis cruelty to keep such beauty so caged,' you said with sadness, then lifted your head to look about us, paying no heed to the flush at my cheeks, 'and unkind to clip the wings of the uncagéd birds so that they cannot fly.'

The retort surpris'd me. Some might have deemed it heresy, for all do know the aviary was created at the bequest of our good king, but for the first time, I observ'd with a sharp sting of sadness how indeed the creatures were imprison'd for our amusement.

'You have not thought,' I ventur'd softly, 'that it is a fate they share with womankind, once she enters matrimony?'

Finally you turn'd to me. My response, I saw, had taken you aback. As, most verily, it had come as a surprise also to myself.

I cannot say where such a strange and bold statement arose from – I suppose it was a matter on my mind. I cannot say whether I made it as a challenge, to goad you such that you would wish to prove me wrong, but within four months we were married. That cold December day, it was – frost in the air. Inside the church I wore a fur-trimmed cloak over my gown, 'twas so chill. My glov'd hand was shaking as the pastor took it to place in yours. I know not whether it was from cold or nerves, but i'faith I declare that my heart did flare with love for you.

As our carriage carried us toward the home you had newly made for us, a fancy took me: 'Let us stop at the park,' I said, 'and revisit where we met. Oh, shall we?!' You would have indulg'd me anything. One arm still link'd around me, you rapp'd with the other hand upon the carriage roof and gave the driver instruction.

How chang'd the park was from that summer afternoon we met. All colour had drain'd away. The sky was a white-grey, harbouring unfallen snow. There was frost upon the rosebeds, and ice sheeted the canal. We made our way quickly, the gravell'd paths cold beneath the thin leather soles of our wedding shoes. Our winter cloaks we pulled tight around us and we press'd close to each other's side, astounded at the novelty of such action being Christian.

It should not have come as surprise that Birdcage Walk would be deserted. The canopied roof of leaves was now but a mesh of bare branches cradling us from above. The peacocks and the parrots were all departed, and the golden cages had been remov'd from the trees; where to, I know not. I imagine a warm interior somewhere in the King's palace, with a fire kept burning at all hours of day and night, and the beautiful gilded cages shimmering in the firelight as the birds inside puff their feathers to trap the warm air while they wait for spring.

I think you knew that the sight of such cold abandon might have brought on melancholy, for in the silence of the empty avenue you turn'd and pull'd me in towards you. I felt my breath catch at the unfamiliarity of such closeness. 'Fear not, mine own wife,' you whisper'd gently, your lips for the first time brushing exquisite across my skin, 'I will not clip your wings.'

My heart quicken'd to think you had remember'd our opening conversation. I could not help but smile.

'Nor I yours,' I whisper'd in return, 'of that I promise.'

And thus, unwitting, I sealed my fate.

I do believe those early months together were as close to heaven as I can hope to know upon this earth. I cannot venture two people have lov'd as fiercely and sublimely as we did. We delighted in each other, we would forget almost that there was a world outside the bedchamber door, and, laughing, remember that we must dress and step outdoors or we should grow pale from lack of daylight. We understood now what it is to unite one's soul with another.

Today, when I feel struck down with melancholy, I remember that time we had together. I thank the lord that he let us taste heaven in all its glory. 'Tis a rare and precious gift indeed and one unglimps'd by most.

For a husband to love his wife even seems worth remarking upon. To love his mistress maybe. But his wife? We are not there to be lov'd, it is not our position. And yet you lov'd me. With certainty can I say that I was more dear to you than anything else you could have owned.

And you, you were everything to me.

It started then with your withdrawal. One night you did not come unto my bedchamber. I waited for you. I kept the candle lit at my bedside. I kept sleep from me until, with a start, I woke in the grey light of dawn and realis'd your absence. The next night was the same. And that which followed. And yet again after that. I fear'd I had unknowingly committed some act that had displeas'd you and I was too afraid to confront you on it for terror that it might mark the end of the very happiness I had grown used to.

By day we made no mention of it. We acted before the servants as if nothing was awry. You spoke kindly to me still. You strok'd my cheeks and held my hand when I was near you. I'd catch you resting your eyes upon me and would swear that their lustre mark'd desire. I was confus'd. Tormented. I could not fathom it. Why? Why did you no longer come to me?

For two full weeks of nights you had not visited in my bedchamber, when at last I heard the door creak open and saw the flicker of candlelight as you enter'd the shadow'd room. Yet a moment before I had been lost in sleep, but now my body thrill'd with anticipation. As I waited beneath the sheets I heard the nervous hesitation in your step as you crossed the floorboards. I believe you were holding your breath. Contrite, I thought. You were waiting for a sign of pardon before you would allow your breath again to pass. In that instant I knew I had not lost your favour.

'My love,' I whisper'd.

That was all. 'Twas enough. Your hand strok'd through the darkness and pull'd back the heavy covers. Into my warm arms I welcom'd you with joy.

'Forgive me,' you said. 'I have neglected you. I fear it pain'd you, but will you believe me when I tell you how I have long'd for your embrace?'

'Yes,' I exclaim'd, 'yes, I have seen it!'

You lower'd your head from mine, spoke in a slim voice. 'You must not worry – I dares't say 'tis but a passing ailment – but i'faith, I have not been feeling,' you paused to find the words, 'not feeling quite of sorts.'

As you said it I knew it for truth, I felt an unaccustom'd fatigue in your touch, a weariness. It frighten'd me. 'But–'

'Shh,' you hush'd, and at that you kiss'd me. Pressing your lips unto mine to stop my questions. You ran your hands over my breast and I sigh'd at the rare pleasure of it. I was limp in your arms. You pull'd my hips towards you. 'You are *most dear* to me,' you said suddenly, with feeling I couldn't understand.

It made me falter. I open'd my eyes again to see you in the candlelight, and reach'd to hug you tightly. I ran my fingers o'er your shoulders, and when they paus'd – as you must have predict'd surely they would – we neither of us let out the breath we held.

Beneath my caress, my fingertips had found a lump – hard, like false bone beneath the flesh. Hesitant now, with mounting fear, their course continued, halting yet when they traced another. These strange lumps terrified me before I knew even what they were.

It was not long after that night I found I was with child. We rejoiced at the lord God's favour. Meantime, we did not speak of your 'ailment' as you had nam'd it, as if we had an understanding that it was something too terrible to voice in words, but I fear'd its portent gravely.

It seem'd the fellow symptoms, unreign'd suddenly, now urg'd themselves apparent. But perhaps in truth it was not so sudden, and only that I was simply more alert now to their presence. Your appetite dwindl'd. Food did not interest you. 'Only a small dish of salad greens,' you would say unto the cook, 'and perhaps a slice or two of bread, that is all I have a taste for.'

It pain'd me more than I can speak of to see how your body lessened while each day mine grew. 'You will waste away to nothing,' I said, afear'd. 'Will you not eat?'

Your eyes, which had been dark always, they alter'd also. Unnaturally bright did they grow, glossy, as if filmed with unshed tears, and rounder than they had been, as if the pupils were enlarging and drowning out the whites. In your now-thin face, they gave you a most disarming look: beady, luminescent.

'Won't you call for the physick?' I would say, knowing my words were to no avail. I think you understood this was not something that he could help you with, not even with his leather bag of potions and scalpels. You preferr'd to deal with it alone, I think.

While my limbs plumpen'd, it seemed yours grew ever more slender. Watching you in the corridor one morning I noted how stalk-like your poor legs had become, poking frail from beneath your breeches. Upon your calves and feet the sorry skin had grown rough and scaly. I sent a servant out for softening creams which, behind a clos'd door, I administer'd unto your skin.

It seem'd to soothe you, but with time your movements grew most jerky, and most skittish. It was a symptom hard to hide from the servants. You slept fitfully, and would start at every unexpected noise. I had to stroke your temples sometimes to calm you. When you came now at night to lie with me, it was as if you had taken residence in a body unfamiliar to myself. So almost weightless were you now, it terrified me. 'Twas as if your bones had hollow'd. Gently, fearing that I might crush you, yet through some awful need to punish and torment myself, I could not resist running my fingertips across the two lumps I had discover'd upon your back. 'Twas cruel torture, for each time I would be left shaking at my powerlessness to halt their progress.

When you began to lose your teeth, when they began to crumble from your mouth, and your lips grew cracked and black and hard like a turtle's shell, funnelled almost, I realis'd you weren't ever again going to be the man I had first known. I am ashamed to admit I griev'd his loss. Was it wrong of me to do so when you were still with me?

Did I know then what was happening to you? Did I really understand so early on? I think I must have. At least, within myself I think I knew.

There was an afternoon, you were sitting in your chair by the window. I was beside you working at a piece of needlework. We were quiet together, unspeaking. The summer evenings were drawing in already. We had missed the season – where did it go? Too much had proved distraction in those past months.

Your poor face was angl'd unto the sky, wan in the pale white-skied light, and I look'd up from pulling my thread at just the moment when across the window a flock of geese flew above in a formation arrow. Swooping south unto where the weather was more clement, the air balmy, the skies blue. Unto lands not yet explor'd by our country's fleet.

I watch'd you follow the swoop of birds with your

eyes, a look of yearning upon your face. And in that moment I knew the inevitable. I knew with the cold dead weight of sureness that you were going to leave me.

When came an autumn afternoon of unexpect'd sun – bright, cool, and clear – you, so frail now, ask'd that we might walk in St James's Park, as once we used to do. I was afear'd. For weeks you had not ventur'd out. It seem'd a breath of wind might have gusted you over. And I knew what could happen. I had been fearing it since the autumn leaves began to fall. There was not long now until winter would be upon us.

Of course you, you must have known already. You said not a thing, but there was a moment, as I was tying the ribbons on my cloak before we left, when I glanc'd up to see you looking at me. 'You are so beautiful,' you said, as if caught in the midst of a private thought.

I knew then that the time had come. I believed I might faint. Collapse upon the hearthstones of the hallway. I bid my tears not to fall and, biting at my lip, turn'd to call for the carriage.

The afternoon was late, and to my relief the park was uncrowded. I was afear'd lest we should see anyone who knew us, how we might explain your chang'd appearance, so we veer'd off the main path beside the canal, and made our way in halting steps across the grass.

I was looking across to a pelican at that moment I sens'd the movement of you departing from me. In a smooth stride I could not have predicted, you shook your heavy woollen cloak unto the grass and gaining speed shook off as well your coat to free yourself.

Had I not been encumbered with child, had I reacted fast enough, perhaps I might have caught you. I know what I had promised you, but in those final moments, I think I might have seiz'd you between my kid-glov'd fingers.

But what then?

Would you have carried me with you? Or would I have held you anchor'd unto the ground?

Thus, I am left alone, remaining with my feet heavy on this earth, and my womb fit to rupture with this child you left within me. It will not be long now until I see him. How will I explain your absence when he grows? How will I shake the terror that one day our child might follow your course and leave me?

Tonight, I went alone to Birdcage Walk and stroll'd under the trees with their embellish'd cages. They will remove them soon – the nights are growing cold already – but for now they do let them hang from the branches for at least a little longer.

I watched the creatures in their gilded prisons, and thought to go along the line, to let the songbirds free. If t'were not for your child, perhaps I might have done so; such action would doubtless end with my head upon the block.

Instead, I halted at the point where first I saw you, and recall'd that heady summer's day.

All around, the birds, trapp'd in their cages, flutter'd and sang and trilled wildly. I clos'd my eyes, and let their song engulf me, until the sound drown'd all other.